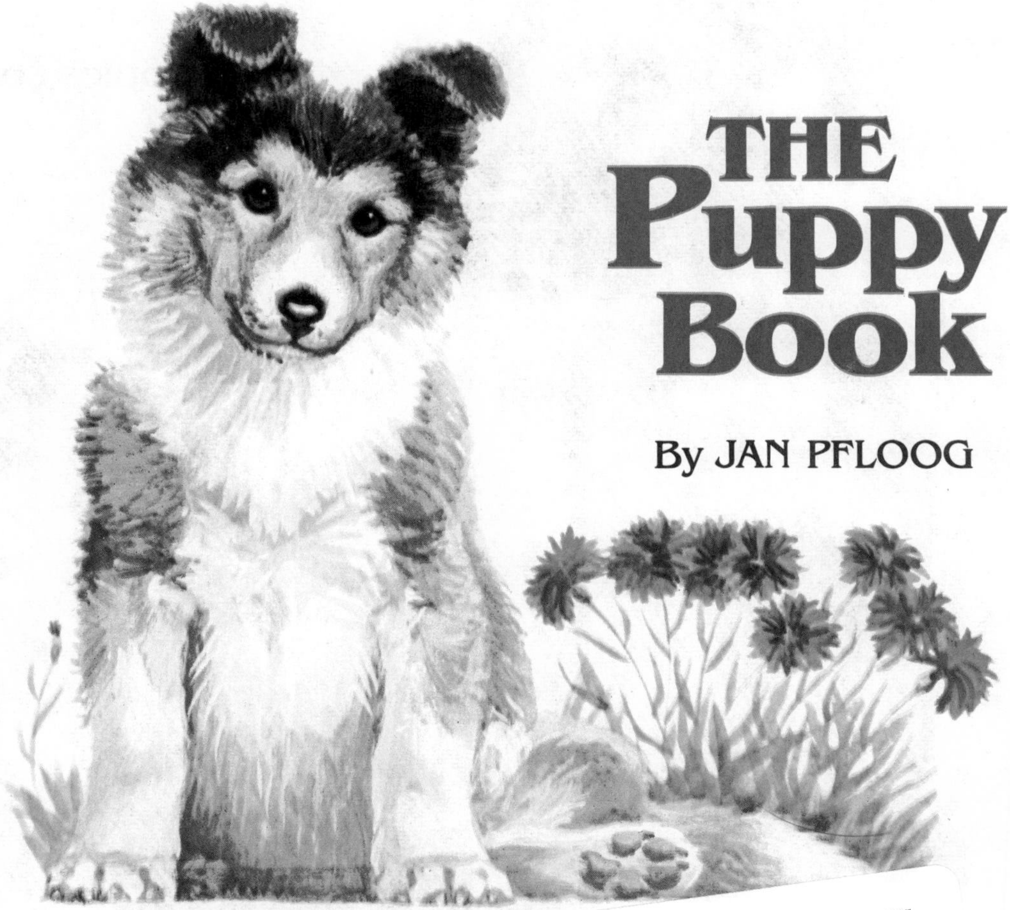

THE Puppy Book

By JAN PFLOOG

A GOLDEN BOOK, N
Western Publishing Company, Inc., R

 ISBN 0-307-58112-8/ISBN 0-307-68946-8 (lib. bdg.) F G H I J

Puppies come

in all sizes, shapes, and colors.

When they eat,

puppies are not very neat.

After eating, puppies like to have a drink.

Sometimes puppies chew on things that are not for eating.

Puppies like to play
better than anything else.

They like to play tug-of-war.

They like to chase a ball.

They chase each other's tail.

Sometimes they even chase their *own* tail!

Some puppies play with cats.

When puppies

get tired, they take a nap.

Sweet dreams, puppies.